Is it a Rock?

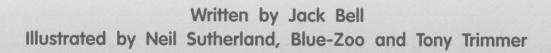

Written by Jack Bell
Illustrated by Neil Sutherland, Blue-Zoo and Tony Trimmer

 can crack. can kick.

Is it a rock?

c can not crack it.

 k can not kick it.

ck ck

 c sticks to k.

c-r-a-ck, crack!

crack! ck ck ck

 c and k can crack it.

It is a pet!